# Santa Claus is Superman

A Book of New Christmas Verse
and Pictures

*Colin M<sup>c</sup>Naughton*

WALKER BOOKS
LONDON

For Mugsy and Fifi

## I'VE SEEN A SNOWMAN FLY!

I've seen a snowman fly,
I have,
I've seen a snowman fly!
I saw it and I ain't mistook,
It wasn't in a picture book:
The snowman stood there, frozen stiff
And I just pushed him off the cliff!
I've seen a snowman fly,
I have,
I've seen a snowman fly.

# IT'S NICE, BUT WHAT IS IT?

Oh, thank you! How kind of you!
Just what I needed!
A blue one with knobs on!
How you have succeeded,
In making my Christmas,
In making my day,
I'm so overwhelmed,
What more can I say?
You shouldn't have bothered,
It must have been dear!
Although there is something
On which I'm not clear –
Its springs are just super,
The fringe on top dandy.
The rocket propulsion
Will come in right handy.
Its drumlins are perfect,
The doobries just right,
The bucket seats comfy,
The lights not too bright.
It's got rudders that shudder
And bloopers that bleep,
Head-rests that rest heads –
It can't have been cheap!
It's a beautiful gift
And its finish exquisite,
Though I have been thinking –
It's nice, but what is it?

# FAT PIG'S LETTER TO SANTA

Dear Father Christmas,
This year I won't be greedy:
You can give all the toys
To the poor and the needy.

Yes, I know a piggy who'd
Be much happier if you'd
Bring him nothing, Father Christmas-
Only FOOD! FOOD! FOOD!

Yours truly
Fat Pig

## THE SECOND WERST POME
## WOT I EVER RITTED

Jingle bells, jingle bells,

Jingle all the way.

Oh what fun it is to ride

On a one-horse open sledge.

## A RICH BOY WOKE ON CHRISTMAS MORN

A rich boy woke on Christmas morn,
   (To tell this doth depress me);
He did not jump for joy, but said,
   "OK then, so impress me!"

### A BRIEF POEM CONCERNING MY EXTREME DISLIKE OF COLD WEATHER

Jack Frost –

Get lost!

## HARD TIMES

We can't afford
  A turkey,
As daddy's out
  of workey.

Though it's not
  very pudgy,
We'll have to eat
  the budgie.

## I'D LEFT IT LATE TO BUY A TREE

I'd left it late to buy a tree –
  They only had one left.
They wanted forty-seven pounds.
  I said, "That's downright theft!
How much? Forty-seven pounds?"
  I shouted at the florist.
"I came in here to buy a tree,
  Not half a bloomin' forest!"

## THE CHRISTMAS STOCKING

I've borrowed a stocking
   From my friend Jim –
He's ever so compliant.
   What's that you say?
It's rather large?
   Well that's cos Jim's a giant!

## SANTA'S SLEIGH

The pictures I've seen of Santa's sleigh –
Well, they must be wrong,
They must be wrong.
It's far too small, that's what I say –
It can't be that long,
No, it can't be that long.

It must be a thousand times that size!

It has to be,

Yes, it has to be!

Like a giant convoy in the skies!

Believe you me,

Believe you me.

My opinion, I know, may come as a shock –

Well, I can't help that,

No, I can't help that.

Each trailer's big as an office block!

Or, I'll eat my hat,

Yes, I'll eat my hat!

So when next Christmas comes around,

I'm in no doubt,

No, I'm in no doubt,

Listen for the sleigh bells' sound –

And check it out,

Check it out!

## IF I HAD A DRAGON

If I had a dragon,
   I'll tell you this, sir:
I'd set it on him,
And I'd set it on her!
   I'd set it on those,
And I'd set it on these.
   I'd set it on anyone –
Just who I please!

   So bring me one, Santa,
And here's what I'll do:
   I promise that I'll
Never set it on you!

## WHAT A CHEEK

I have noticed you up in your sleigh, sir,
    And there's something I feel I must say, sir:
There's a strong likelihood,
    You eat more than you should –
Father Christmas, you're too fat! Good day, sir!

## THERE'S NO PLACE LIKE HOME

*To the tune of "I'm Dreaming of a White Christmas"*

I'm dreaming of a green Christmas,
Just like the ones I used to know,
Where the ice beasts glisten,
And swamp bugs listen,
And slime slugs quiver to and fro –

Oh, I'm dreaming . . .

## SANTA CLAUS IS SUPERMAN!

I was lying in bed the other night
    When suddenly, I saw the light!
It's clear as day, I must be right –
    Santa Claus is Superman!

I've been cunning, used my wits,
    I've pieced together all the bits.
And glory be! The whole thing fits:
    Santa Claus is Superman!

Where's Clark Kent on Christmas Eve?
    In Smallville, he'd have you believe.
What do you think I am? Naive?
    Santa Claus is Superman!

And where's Father Christmas the rest of the year?
    Funny how he just seems to – disappear.
He's in Metropolis – it's clear!
    Santa Claus is Superman!

You might say it's a pack of lies –
    One's dark, one's fair – they're a different size.
Haven't you heard the word "disguise"?
    Santa Claus is Superman!

Tell me who else has the speed,
    I mean, the kind of speed you'd need?
It's obvious, are we agreed?
    Santa Claus is Superman!

And who else is there strong enough,
    To carry all that Christmas stuff?
Admit it now, I know it's tough:
    Santa Claus *is* Superman!

# THE NATIVITY PLAY

Kamal is a shepherd,
　Mark is a king,
Doha's a nangel,
　Pete has to sing.

Tracy's a wise man,
　Kim is one too,
Shirley's the other one;
　Tom just says "moo"!

David's a donkey,
　The twins are the straw,
Ike is a sheepdog,
　Shamin's a door.

Zoë's the innkeeper,
　(After a row!),
Mo's a nother nangel,
　And Vicky's a cow.

As for the star parts,
　Of course there was no fuss –
Joanne will be Mary
And I will be – JOFUS!

## THE CAROL SINGERS

"After three –
One, two, three."

"Good King Wens los las-lish losh . . ."
"One, two, three."
"Good King Wenlas losh lif laf . . ."
"One, two, three."
"Good King Wenslosch – lis-last-louse . . ."
"One, two, three."
"Good King Wenschlershloshlashschlisch . . ."

. . .whisper, whisper, whisper. . .

"One, two, three . . ."

**"Sa – hi – lent night,
Ho – oh – lee night . . ."**

# THE SONG OF THE PUDDING HUNTERS

Once a year, in mid-December,

(The month of Christmas, you'll remember),

The bravest men do sally forth,

To hunt the pudding in the frozen north.

CHORUS:     Oh, the pudding hunt, the pudding hunt,

Tally ho to the Christmas pudding hunt!

We all converge by different means:

In cars and trucks and flying machines.

Yes, the bravest men are always found

At the ancient pudding hunting ground!

CHORUS:     Oh, the pudding . . .

No, the pudding hunters show no fear,

We hunt the pudding with club and spear.

So stuff the turkey, peel the spuds,

We're off to hunt for Christmas puds.

CHORUS:    Oh, the pudding . . .

The slaughter is a dreadful sight,

(Those puddings put up quite a fight),

Brandy butter stains the snow,

As the hunters bag their puds and go!

CHORUS:    Oh, the pudding . . .

Arriving home on Christmas Eve,

On to the table with a heave,

A big fat pudding, firm and sweet –

The Christmas feast is now complete.

CHORUS:    Oh, the pudding . . .

## THE WEATHER NEVER BOTHERS ME

I went to see my friend today,
To see if he'd come out to play.
He said, "No fear, you must be mad,
I'm staying at home with Mum and Dad!
It's freezing cold – it's minus three!"
He slammed the door and turned the key.
I'm mystified, I'm all at sea,
He's soft as clarts – he has to be.
The weather never bothers me!

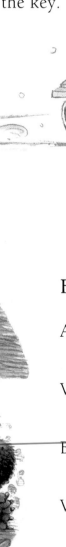

*Burp!*

## FEAST OF STEPHEN

A hungry grizzly bear looked out
  On the feast of Stephen,
When the snow lay round about,
  Deep and crisp and even:
Brightly shone the moon that night,
  Though the frost was cruel,
When a poor man came in sight,
  The grizzly bear did droo-oo-el!
(Then he ate him!)

## EDWARD'S PRESENT

They're saying Edward's present
May have been a great mistake.
    I tried to warn them –
Not a bit of notice did they take!
    "The Complete Junior Woodwork Kit",
It said upon the lid.
    And I will now relate to you
What naughty Edward did:
    To the floor he nailed the carpet –
(My folks were still in bed),
    And then he nailed the sofa down –
(In case of storms, he said).
    With a drill which worked on batteries,
He made holes in all the doors.
    With his "Master Carpenter Mallet"
Smashed the chocolate Santa Claus!
    The clockwork-driven chainsaw
Was next to catch his eye;
    He wound it up and switched it on –
That's when I said goodbye!
    But as he'd nailed the doors shut,
There was no way I could flee.
    And Edward shouted, "TIMBER!"
As he felled the Christmas tree.
    By the time that Mum and Dad broke in,
The damage had been done.
    And Edward simply smiled and said,
"I've never had such fun!"

Timber!

## OH, NO! NOT AGAIN!

Oh, no! Not again!
Every year, it's the same:
    Underpants from Aunt Elaine,
Elephants from Auntie Jane!

## WHAT DID YOU GET?

On Christmas morning, Bill and I met;
"Hi there, Billy. What did you get?"

"A football strip and a cricket bat,
    A furry Davy Crockett hat,
A Beano and a Dandy book,
    An'-one-about-a-man-called-Captain-Hook!
Shin pads and a pair of socks,
    A jigsaw and a selection box.
A hymn book by a bloke called Wesley,
    An' 'The golden greats of Elvis Presley'."

"Well, tweedledum and tweedledee!
You got just the same as me!"

# HOW FATHER CHRISTMAS GETS INTO HOUSES
## WITHOUT CHIMNEYS

inking –

eep,

dder

n't

**SCOTLAND YARN**
**LONDON**

Dear Mr McNaughton,

    I'm afraid I cannot allow this poem to be published as it contains information likely to be used by burglars and other nasty types to commit crimes.

    Yours sincerely,

_P. Whigpo_

THE CHIEF OF POLICE

It's

It's

And

It ca

P.S. I had no idea that's how Santa did it!

# SLEEP TIGHT, FATHER CHRISTMAS

On Christmas Day while we're all playing:
   Stuffing our faces – in church praying,
You know what Santa Claus is doing?
   (No, not skiing or canoeing);
You may think it's rather boring,
   But he's in bed asleep and snoring!

Poor old Santa – work's all done,
Let him sleep while we have fun –
Deserves it more than anyone.
Sleep tight, Father Christmas.